Alison Bell's

MORE GRADED PIECES FOR PIANO

BOOK 2 : EASY

Exclusive distributors:
Music Sales Limited, 8/9 Frith Street, London W1V 5TZ. England.
Music Sales Pty Limited, 120 Rothschild Avenue, Rosebery, NSW 2018, Australia.

This book © Copyright 1990 Wise Publications
Order No. AM78817/ISBN 0.7119.2173.3

Art direction by Mike Bell. Book designed by Evelina Frescura
Cover photography by Peter Wood
Typeset by Capital Setters

Music Sales' complete catalogue lists thousands of titles and is free
from your local music shop, or direct from Music Sales Limited. Please send £1 in stamps
for postage to Music Sales Limited, 8/9 Frith Street, London W1V 5TZ.

Printed in the United Kingdom by
J.B. Offset Printers (Marks Tey) Limited, Marks Tey, Essex.

ANNIE'S SONG

WORDS & MUSIC: JOHN DENVER

I0633711

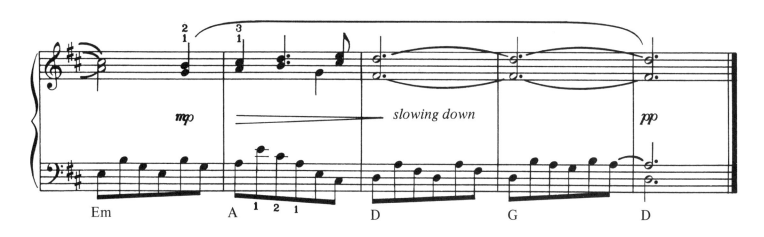

LUCY IN THE SKY WITH DIAMONDS

WORDS & MUSIC: JOHN LENNON & PAUL McCARTNEY

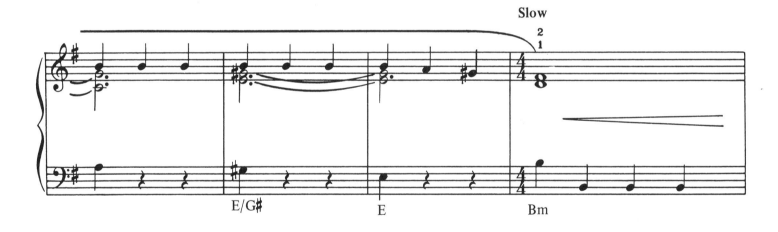

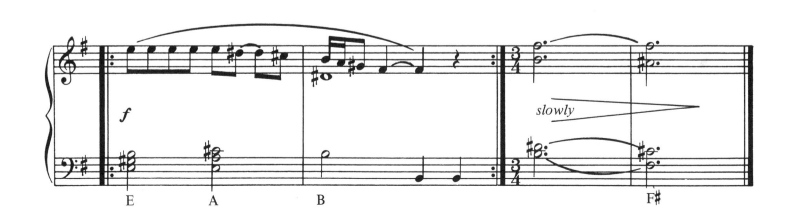

BORN IN THE USA

WORDS & MUSIC: BRUCE SPRINGSTEEN

DON'T CRY FOR ME ARGENTINA

MUSIC: ANDREW LLOYD WEBBER
LYRICS: TIM RICE

LAND OF HOPE & GLORY
(Pomp & Circumstance March)

COMPOSER: SIR EDWARD ELGAR

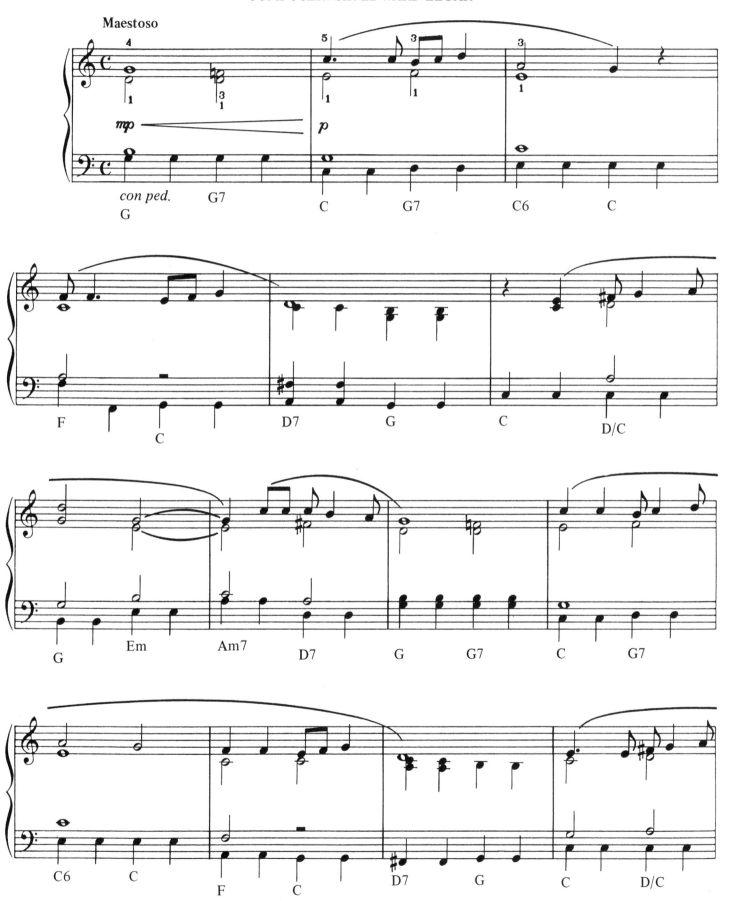

WILLOW WALTZ

MUSIC: CYRIL WATTERS

SHOW ME THE WAY TO GO HOME

WORDS & MUSIC: IRVING KING

SPANISH EYES

WORDS: CHARLES SINGLETON, EDDIE SNYDER
MUSIC: BERT KAEMPFERT

Moderate Latin

ESO BESO

WORDS & MUSIC: JOE & NOEL SHERMAN

SIDE BY SIDE

WORDS & MUSIC: HARRY WOODS

FIDDLER ON THE ROOF

MUSIC: JERRY BOCK
LYRICS: SHELDON HARNICK

I LOVE TO CRY AT WEDDINGS

WORDS & MUSIC: CY COLEMAN & DOROTHY FIELDS

FLY ME TO THE MOON (In Other Words)

WORDS & MUSIC: BART HOWARD

SUPER TROUPER

WORDS & MUSIC: BENNY ANDERSSON & BJORN ULVAEUS

ON WINGS OF SONG

COMPOSER: FELIX MENDELSSOHN

ZACATECAS

WORDS & MUSIC: MILTON LEEDS & TED VARNICK

C7   F

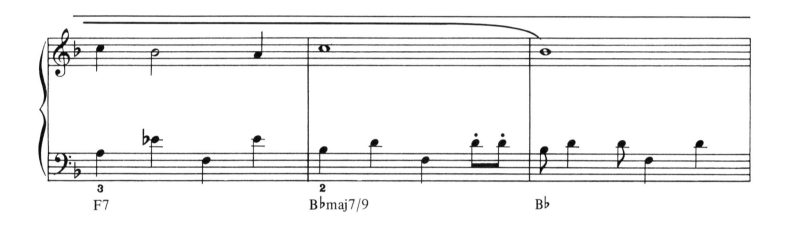

F7   B♭maj7/9   B♭

D7   G7   C7

C7   F6